CONTENTS

Haigh Clough looking towards Pule Hill

INTRODUCTION

The BBC's "Last of the Summer Wine" has made our local area familiar to many people. Walkers and cyclists in the countryside are interested in finding out how landscape features have developed. Others visit viewpoints like Castle Hill or Holme Moss and want to know more about the scenery.

Huddersfield's three main sources of industrial wealth, the textile, engineering and chemical industries all have links with Huddersfield's underlying rocks. The early iron industry in the medieval period developed because there was iron-ore associated with the Coal Measures in the eastern part of the district. Sandstone was used to make millstones for grinding corn in the middle ages, so rocks in the western part of the district became known as 'Millstone Grit', although there are other sorts of rocks here as well as sandstones. Later, the sandstones were used for building stone, in particular for good quality construction stone, and for roofing 'slates' and flags. 'York stone' from West Yorkshire is well-known throughout the country and is still produced in several large local quarries.

Woollen textiles, which largely created the wealth of industrial West Yorkshire, needed water for power in the early days, and for cleaning and processing the wool into cloth. This was provided by the water bearing rocks of the Millstone Grit sandstones. The local chemical industry (including dyestuffs) also grew from the needs of the woollen industry, and is still a major employer. Engineering was stimulated by a need for machinery in the textile industry, and may have used local iron and steel in the early days. Coal in the Holme Valley and to the east of Huddersfield was used for both domestic and industrial use. When accessible coal ran out, exploitation moved to deeper mines to the east, some of which still operated until recently.

o o o O O O o o o

This booklet, which follows our previous publication *"Guide to the Building Stones of Huddersfield"*, is for anyone who wishes to know more about the rocks and scenery, and in particular those who walk in the district. The local rocks consist of sandstones and shales laid down horizontally and only slightly disturbed since, so the structures and geology are not difficult to understand. There are sections on rocks and weathering in the National Curriculum and we hope that teachers will be able to use the information and localities to show their pupils good examples of the features they are asked to study.

The first time a geological term is used it is underlined, and explained in the glossary. Where possible we have explained new words in the context of the writing, and hope that people unfamiliar with geology are not put off by the terminology. The bibliography lists the geological references and sources. Localities mentioned on the inside back cover are suggestions for people who would like to study the rocks at closer quarters.

LANDSCAPES

This part of West Yorkshire reveals many contrasting landscapes, from scenes of industrialisation in the main valleys to sparsely populated moorland valued for its recreational use and rugged beauty. The present scenery is a reflection of how geological processes operating over millions of years have moulded the original rock foundations into the hills and valleys of today. The landscape is continually changing in response to the earth's natural processes and human activity.

From the summit of Castle Hill near Almondbury can be seen varied landscapes, from the bleak Pennine gritstone moors to the gentler countryside stretching out to the east. Deeply cut into the landscape, the valleys (cloughs) carry fast flowing streams to the main rivers. On the gentler slopes above the valleys, villages and farms can be seen scattered across the landscape with distinctive patterns of dry stone walls and hedges enclosing cultivated land.

The underlying rocks have played an important role in the development of this Pennine landscape. The <u>Millstone Grit Series</u> and <u>Coal Measures</u> comprise alternate beds or layers of <u>sandstones</u> and <u>shales</u> with different rates of <u>erosion</u>. The harder sandstones create distinct landforms known as benches or plateaux, whilst the softer and more easily eroded shales form the steeper valley slopes. Some over-deepening of the Colne and Holme valleys occurred towards the end of the

View from Castle Hill towards Meltham and West Nab

rivers of the Colne and Holme valleys lie hidden from view as they flow from upland sources towards the industrial town of Huddersfield. The town is located at the confluence of the Colne and Holme valleys where there is relatively flat ground formed by the lowest beds of the <u>Coal Measures</u>. From the higher ground, wooded tributary

last Ice Age, approximately 15,000 years ago. Rising temperatures melted immense quantities of snow and ice from the frozen ground. The release of this vast amount of post-glacial melt water deepened the two valleys, erosion being promoted by a lack of any vegetation cover.

COAL MEASURE LANDSCAPES

The regional tilt of the local rock is eastward. The <u>weathering</u> and erosion of rock strata has created a series of escarpments with steep westward facing scarp slopes and gentler <u>dip</u> slopes to the east.

Beneath these escarpments, hidden in the depths of the Holme valley, lies the boundary between the Coal Measures and the older Rough Rock which forms the uppermost bed of the Millstone Grit. Further benches of Grenoside and Greenmoor sandstones have provided flat, well-drained sites for the nearby

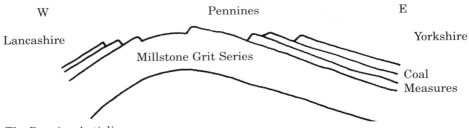

The Pennine <u>Anticline</u>

To the north west from Castle Hill, sandstone beds form the Hall Bower and Newsome benches, with shales forming the intervening steep slopes of the Coal Measures escarpments.

villages of Almondbury to the east, and Farnley Tyas and Shepley to the south east, where many of the traditional stone buildings are built from locally quarried sandstone.

Coal Measures landscape overlooking Thunderbridge

MILLSTONE GRIT LANDSCAPES

West of Castle Hill beyond the Holme Valley, the Coal Measures have been removed by erosion. Underlying beds of Millstone Grit have weathered into west facing gritstone escarpments such as Pule Hill and Standedge. Many of these edges have eroded into strange shaped blocks and boulders. Gritstone deciduous woodland found at Royd House Wood, Farnley Bank and Carr Wood. The valley below seems too deep for the small Rushfield Dike running north eastward, which may be described as a 'misfit stream', suggesting that the valley was previously shaped by a much larger and more powerful river, perhaps glacial meltwater.

Castle Hill seen from Honley showing benches

edges characterise Pennine landscapes, often forming a series of landmarks, proudly standing out against distant skylines.

Eastwards from Castle Hill towards Fenay Beck and Kirkburton the landscape takes on a gentler appearance, influenced by the underlying shales of the Coal Measures and the relative lack of thick sandstones. Clay soils, developed from the weathering of shales, led to the establishment of pleasant stretches of

To the east of Fenay Beck, Lepton Edge forms the next escarpment, with the villages of Emley, Flockton and Grange Moor on sandstone benches, which dip gently at about 5° to the east. This scarp and dip landscape, although not visible from Castle Hill, continues further to the east beyond the district, where the Woolley Edge escarpment forms high ground beyond West Bretton.

The highest terrain of the district lies to the south-west where Huddersfield White Rock sandstone underlies the peat-covered moors of Black Hill and Holme Moss. On this treeless and exposed landscape only resilient mosses, moor grasses and the distinctive cotton grass can survive in the harsh climate on impoverished acid soils which develop from a quartz rich sandstone. In places where vegetation has been removed by acid rain and erosion, the exposed peat is cut into deep drainage channels. The flanks of these upland gritstone plateaux are dissected by numerous steep rocky cloughs, often containing waterfalls where streams tumble over alternate beds of soft shales and resistant sandstones.

Natural processes are continually modifying the landscape. On steep slopes such as March Hill, north west of March Haigh Reservoir near Marsden, and West Nab near Meltham, down-slope movements have resulted in landslips.

The upland areas receive high levels of rainfall and are the source

Peat Grough, Wessenden Head Moor

of much of the district's water supply, as they replenish the numerous reservoirs dotted across the landscape. This stored water is used mainly for Yorkshire Water's public supply, but also by local industry, and to maintain the Huddersfield Narrow Canal's water level. The rocks of an area are often revealed in the selection of materials used for the building of houses and dry stone walls. In many Pennine villages

Slumping in shales above March Haigh Reservoir

Shale Gully on Castleshaw Moor

and farms, the use of locally quarried sandstone creates a distinctive landscape where dark weathered buildings blend naturally into the local scenery. The use of hedges and fences as field boundaries indicates the presence of shales and the scarcity, or even absence, of local sandstones. In many areas of the Coal Measures, where shales and clays form a high percentage of the underlying rock, bricks were often locally manufactured and replaced sandstone as the predominant building material.

View from Pule Hill towards Green Owlers

ROCKS

The rocks in the Huddersfield district are all <u>sedimentary</u>, which means that they have been formed by the deposition of sand or clay particles in deltas, flood plains, river channels or the sea. All Huddersfield rocks are of late <u>Carboniferous</u> age, and are between about 320 and 305 million years old. The older rocks are the Millstone Grit series of <u>Namurian</u> age; following them are the Coal Measures of <u>Westphalian</u> age. The area which was to become Britain was, at that time, near the equator with a hot and humid climate. Shallow shelf seas, low lying flood-plains and deltas covered most of Britain, but there was a northern landmass lying where the Highlands of Scotland are now, from which large rivers drained southwards. They carried huge amounts of clay and sand which were deposited wherever the currents slowed down. Deposition of sediment took place in river channels, flood-plains and lagoons close to sea

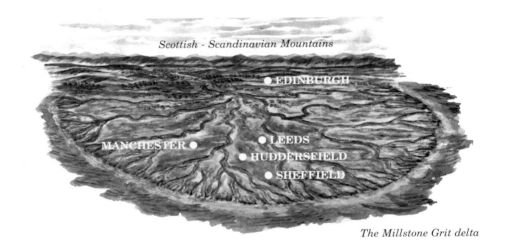

Scottish - Scandinavian Mountains

EDINBURGH

MANCHESTER
LEEDS
HUDDERSFIELD
SHEFFIELD

The Millstone Grit delta

Ryecroft Edge Quarry, Linthwaite

BEDDING PLANE

J O I N T

level, and deltas were built out as the rivers carried material into the sea. Various types of sedimentary rocks occurred in these different environments of deposition.

ROCK STRUCTURES

Sedimentary rocks are usually bedded which means they are in definite layers (beds) of a single rock type with a break above and below called a bedding-plane. Each bed of sandstone was probably laid down within a fairly short period of time and the bedding-plane represents an interval when deposition ceased.

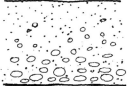

Graded Bedding

further type of massive bed which develops at the edge of the delta front where slumped sediment avalanches down to the basin floor. The speed of this action gives no time for internal layering to occur, although a sorting of grain sizes (known as graded bedding) develops from the suspended load.

Many of the Millstone Grit sandstones have preserved within them a series of low angled beds and bedding planes known as <u>cross-bedding</u>. These beds

Bingley Quarry, Digley showing cross-bedding

Some sandstones have massive bedding, with beds that can be several metres thick. These massive beds probably developed in a river channel where sediment was laid down from a fast-flowing current carrying a large volume of suspended sediment. These currents then experienced a rapid decrease in velocity and the suspended load was dropped suddenly. This rapid deposition is also characteristic of a

formed as sandbanks on the inside bend of a meandering river channel where water velocity was lower, and finer sediment was deposited. It is clear from the scale of the cross-bedding that some of the channels were 0.5 to 1km wide, and up to 40m deep, similar to the present deltas of the Indus in Pakistan, and Brahmaputra-Ganges in Bangladesh.

Flaggy bedding has bedding-planes about 2 to 5cms apart, and was formed in calmer conditions in shallow waters in the delta, where there was a regular slow supply of sediment deposited at intervals. These beds are ideal for use as flagstones for paving and 'slates' for roofs.

ROCK MINERALS

Sandstones are mainly composed of grains of the hard mineral quartz. These quartz grains are usually angular when smaller than about 0.15mm, but rounded by attrition when larger. The name 'grit' is used for many local sandstones and indicates the coarseness of the quartz grains in the rock, although the size of the particles in the sandstones is variable. Most of the sandstones of the Millstone Grit are coarse, with grains larger than 0.5mm and there are white quartz pebbles up to 10mm, especially in the Kinderscout Grit. Medium and fine-grained sandstones are found in the Huddersfield White Rock and in the sandstones of the Coal Measures.

Some local sandstone beds contain substantial amounts of the mineral feldspar, which decomposes more readily than quartz. Its presence gives an indication of the geology of the eroding northern landmass from which the rivers carried sediment. Feldspar is common in igneous granites and metamorphic gneisses, rocks still found in the Scottish Highlands.

Other minerals are found in trace amounts throughout the sandstones but especially in the Kinderscout Grit and the Rough Rock, though a geological microscope is needed to identify them. These include garnet, rutile, zircon and tourmaline which are typical minerals of some metamorphic and igneous rocks, as well as the unusual mineral monazite found in some Scottish and Scandinavian granites, again suggesting that the origin of all local Carboniferous sediments was the northern landmass. Most flaggy sandstones contain flakes of a mineral called muscovite mica which appears white and shiny and reflects light like a mirror. Mica breaks up into small bright flakes which are easily carried in river currents. In still water, away from the main channels, muscovite flakes were the last to settle on the bottom and coat the bedding-planes of flaggy sandstones.

Carbon is also a common mineral in some sandstone beds. Forests on the delta plain just above sea level, contributed branches, roots and leaves which floated down the rivers. Large branches and roots caught on sand-banks are sometimes preserved as fossils in cross-bedded sandstones. Leaves which drifted into stagnant water decomposed to carbon which was left on bedding-planes to be buried by later sand deposits. The black flakes in the Rough Rock would have originated in this way. In the Readycon Dean sandstones there are thin black films of carbon on some bedding-planes. Towards the top of the Millstone Grit series, thin coal seams, several centimetres in thickness become more common. Some are thick enough to be worked in early pits, for example, the Upper Meltham coal.

ENVIRONMENTS OF DEPOSITION

The coarsest sediments were deposited in the channels of the fastest flowing rivers while finer sediments, after prolonged sorting, settled on the river banks and the delta front. The finest clay particles, carried in suspension by the rivers, were either washed overbank or taken out to sea to settle slowly. Each thin bed of clay became black or grey shale after burial by later deposits. The beds are so fine that the bedding is described as laminated. Clay minerals are rich in iron at some horizons, so the black or dark grey shales often have a brown or yellow colouration when exposed to weathering at the surface. Marine animals were easily fossilised in this low energy environment where there

Fossil Bark

was a lack of wave or current action. Bivalves, brachiopods and goniatites are common in shale beds (called <u>marine bands</u>) where the huge numbers of fossils found must have resulted from a change in the animals' environment at the time.

<u>Lithification</u> takes place at depth after the sediments of sand and clay have been laid down, when water is squeezed out by pressure from later deposits. Cracks and fractures known as joints are caused by movements and stresses within the earth's crust. When rocks

Tree Fossil in Clockface Quarry

are exposed to weathering, at or near the surface joints are opened up. Shales are fissile, which means they split easily along their bedding-planes and often crumble when the joints are close together.

Massive sandstones are particularly resistant to weathering and often form scars and cliff features called 'edges' in the district. Sandstones vary in colour from pale grey Huddersfield White Rock to the rich orange of the Readycon Dean and the Rough Rock sandstones, the latter to be found in Beaumont Park and Longwood Edge. This colouration and staining results from iron in the shales moving in solution during burial and compaction of the sediments. The joints and bedding planes within the sandstones provide an easy route for the iron solution to move. This may then be re-deposited as brown iron staining, (Liesegang Rings), which can readily be seen on freshly quarried stone and on flags such as the Greenmoor Sandstone in St George's Square, Huddersfield.

The Namurian and Westphalian strata are geologically significant in that their sediments follow a cyclic pattern of deposition repeated many times. These cycles of strata deposition, are called cyclothems and reflect the changing environment of deposition, from marine shale followed by non-marine floodplain and deltaic shales and sandstones, and finally seat-earth and coal, after which marine transgression started the cycle again. Cyclothems vary in thickness suggesting that subsidence of the basin was local and perhaps irregular.

One scenario put forward by geologists

is that the area south of the northern landmass was a basin which was slowly subsiding due to the overlying weight and compaction of new sediment being laid down. It is likely that the water was never deep in many parts of the delta system, with the depositional surface fluctuating around sea level. At times the sea encroached onto the land as a marine transgression and the

Liesegang Rings

sedimentation cycle began again. At other times the delta built up sufficiently above sea level and remained there long enough for forests to grow and provide material for future seams of coal. Abundant plant material falling onto waterlogged ground decomposed slowly allowing swamp peat to accumulate. The peat was then compressed at depth over millions of years. Carbon became concentrated, as water and gases were driven off by higher temperatures and pressures, and coal was formed.

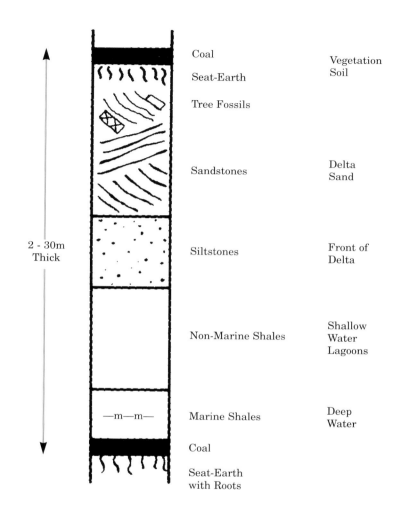

	Coal	Vegetation
	Seat-Earth	Soil
	Tree Fossils	
	Sandstones	Delta Sand
2 - 30m Thick	Siltstones	Front of Delta
	Non-Marine Shales	Shallow Water Lagoons
	Marine Shales	Deep Water
	Coal	
	Seat-Earth with Roots	

A Coal Measure Cyclothem

Other examples of marine transgressions are associated with world-wide rising sea levels. These were probably due to the forming and melting of ice sheets which developed over the southern polar landmass at this time. Melting of the ice sheets made sea level rise, causing a transgression. It then fell again as ice sheets built up during colder periods. In the Carboniferous strata of Northern Europe the fossil record reflects these changing environmental conditions.

FOSSILS

Deltas of the Carboniferous period were heavily forested but the plant species were quite different from those of today. Tree ferns grew up to 15m high in an equatorial climate of high temperatures and heavy rainfall. *Calamites*, a member of the horsetail family of today, grew to tree size. Seed ferns such as *Neuropteris* which often fossilise beautifully with fern-like leaves were then abundant but are now extinct. Club mosses, such as *Lepidodendron*, characterised by spores held in cones, also grew to large sizes.

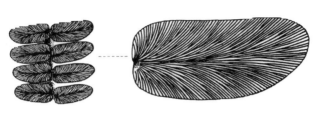

Neuropteris x 1/2

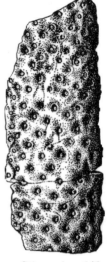

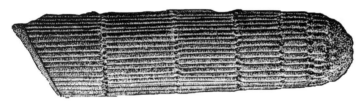

Calamites x 1/2

Stigmaria x 1/2

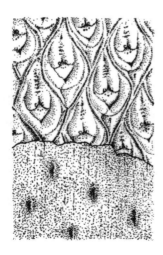

*Large branch of
Lepidodendron x 3/4*

*Leafy branch of
Lepidodendron x 1*

For plants to become fossilised, rapid covering with sediment or sinking into the stagnant water of the delta marshes is necessary. This prevents organic material in the plant being lost to the atmosphere as carbon dioxide. Leaves may be well preserved in fine-grained mudstones and shales but are broken up during turbulent current action, with leaf fragments found as black flecks in sandstones, a characteristic feature of the Rough Rock. An impression of a leaf or branch is often represented only by a black carbon film.

the east of the Huddersfield district, sometimes have leaf and branch fossils. A large *Stigmaria* tree-trunk found at Hoyle's Quarry, Crosland Hill in 1962, stands at the entrance to the Tolson Museum, Ravensknowle Park, Huddersfield.

The sea, which periodically covered the deltas and flood-plains, was rich in life. *Dunbarella* was a thin-shelled bivalve which probably swam through the sea like present day scallops. Another shelled animal was the brachiopod *Lingula*.

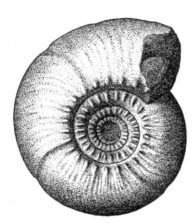  

Gastrioceras x 1   *Lingula x 3*

Trees and branches brought down by heavy floods and stranded on sand banks are sometimes preserved in cross-bedded sandstones. Roots and rootlets are often preserved in the soil and sand in which they grew. Quartz-rich soils lithified to produce a tough white sandstone called ganister, frequently containing black rootlets in situ.

Many local sandstones contain plant fossils so a search of quarries is often rewarding. Coal Measures shales, to

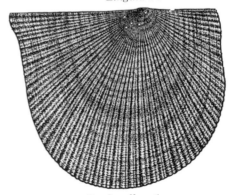

Dunbarella x 1

GEOLOGICAL MAP of the HUDDERSFIELD DISTRICT

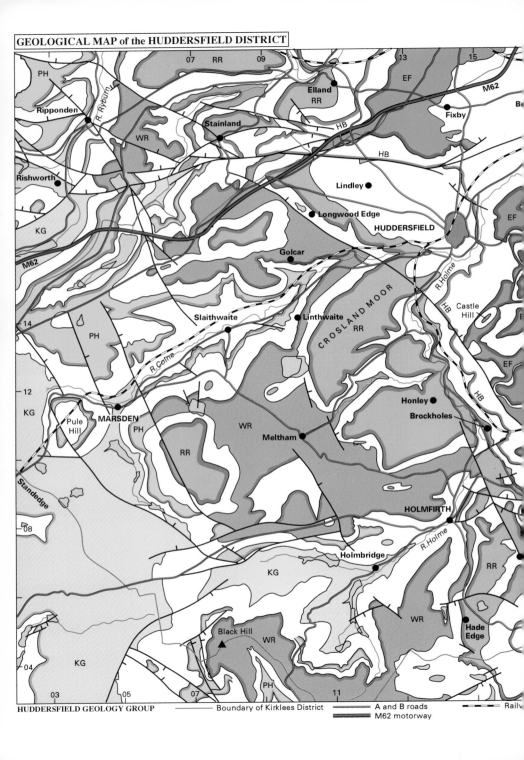

07   RR   09   13   15

PH   EF   M62

Ripponden   R. Ryburn   Elland   Fixby   B
                              RR
              Stainland
         WR   HB

Rishworth   HB

KG   Lindley

M62   Longwood Edge

                                             HUDDERSFIELD

                        Golcar   EF

                                          R. Holme

14   CROSLAND MOOR   Castle
PH   Slaithwaite   Linthwaite   RR   Hill

                           R. Colne   HB

12
KG   EF

      Pule   MARSDEN
      Hill   PH   WR   Honley
         RR   Meltham   Brockholes

Standedge   HB

08   HOLMFIRTH

                                             R. Holme

                              KG   Holmbridge   RR

04   WR

      KG   Black Hill   WR   Hade
                          ▲   Edge

      03   05   PH   07   11

HUDDERSFIELD GEOLOGY GROUP ——— Boundary of Kirklees District ════ A and B roads ━━━ Railw
                                           ▬▬ M62 motorway

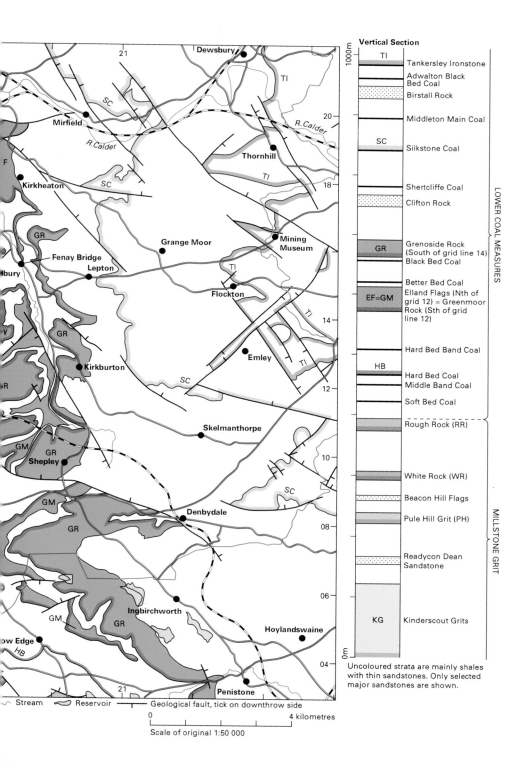

Vertical Section

1000m

TI — Tankersley Ironstone

Adwalton Black
Bed Coal

Birstall Rock

Middleton Main Coal

SC — Silkstone Coal

Shertcliffe Coal

Clifton Rock

GR — Grenoside Rock
(South of grid line 14)
Black Bed Coal

Better Bed Coal

EF=GM — Elland Flags (Nth of
grid 12) = Greenmoor
Rock (Sth of grid
line 12)

Hard Bed Band Coal

HB — Hard Bed Coal
Middle Band Coal

Soft Bed Coal

Rough Rock (RR)

White Rock (WR)

Beacon Hill Flags

Pule Hill Grit (PH)

Readycon Dean
Sandstone

KG — Kinderscout Grits

0m

LOWER COAL MEASURES

MILLSTONE GRIT

Uncoloured strata are mainly shales
with thin sandstones. Only selected
major sandstones are shown.

Dewsbury

21

SC

Mirfield

R. Calder

R. Calder

Thornhill

20

TI

18

Kirkheaton

SC

TI

F

GR

Grange Moor

Mining
Museum

Fenay Bridge
Lepton

bury

TI

Flockton

GR

14

Emley

TI

Kirkburton

SC

TI

12

R

Skelmanthorpe

y

10

GM

GR

SC

Shepley

GM

Denbydale

GR

08

GR

06

Ingbirchworth

GR

Hoylandswaine

GM

w Edge

HB

04

21

Penistone

Stream   Reservoir   Geological fault, tick on downthrow side

0   4 kilometres

Scale of original 1:50 000

Goniatites, the ancestors of ammonites, were free-swimming marine animals. They could propel themselves by squirting streams of water and would have moved jerkily. Goniatites are small in size. They are concentrated in beds of shale (marine bands), along with bivalve and brachiopod fossils. Examining fossils with a handlens will subsequently filled with silica, calcite or pyrite to produce a cast. Sometimes after the shell is buried, calcite or iron minerals can accumulate around the fossil and form nodules. Those made of calcite are called bullions and often contain uncrushed goniatites, examples of which have been found at Scammonden Reservoir. Ironstone

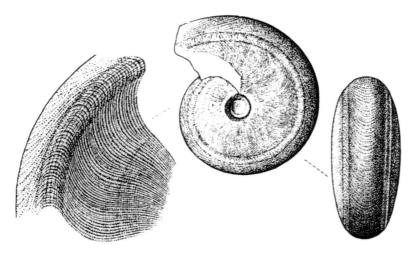

Goniatite - Reticuloceras bilingue x 1 $^1/_2$

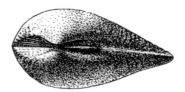

Carbonicola x $^1/_2$

enable you to see the fine ornament, characteristic for each species. The marine band on Pule Hill is well exposed, and a thin marine band outcrops near Brockholes.

Shells themselves can be preserved directly by rapid burial in sand or mud. In other cases the shell dissolves leaving a mould in the rock which is nodules are common in both shales and sandstones and are often found with *Carbonicola* fossils in the Coal Measures. *Carbonicola* was a fresh-water bivalve shaped rather like the present day mussel. Most fossils are compressed when the sediments become compacted by further burial. This flattening and distorting can make them difficult to identify.

Sandstones sometimes record evidence of animals living in or on sand banks of deltas. Feeding tracks of invertebrates show as irregular furrows (in the sandstones) and both 'worm' burrows and worm casts are often found. These are known as trace fossils. Fossils represent only a fraction of the animals and plants that would have lived in the Carboniferous deltas and seas. Some creatures would have been preyed upon by predators such as large active shark-like fish with fins supported by spines and tough scaly skins. The jaw of a shark-like fish fossil called *Edestus newtoni* was found in 1915 during the sinking of a well at Rock Mills near Brockholes. It was found in shales below the Rough Rock and was presented to the Museum of Natural History by Elon Crowther, a director of the firm Sykes and Co. It is now held at British Geological Survey headquarters at Keyworth, Nottinghamshire.

The use of fossils to match or correlate rocks found in different regions has always been of great value. The fossils found in marine bands in shales of this district are of international significance because each marine band is characterised by its own species of goniatite. Marine bands can be traced across Northern Europe from Britain to Ukraine. Goniatites are particularly useful as they were widespread and evolved rapidly, with their shells changing in ornament and pattern. W. S. Bisat published the fundamental paper after years of research in Yorkshire and Lancashire distinguishing and naming the important goniatite species, which enabled geologists to correlate the Millstone Grit strata with confidence. Nowadays micro-fossils, particularly plant spores, which are small, resistant and widely found in shales and coal seams, are also used for correlation.

The Brockholes Fish

WEATHERING

Sandstones and shales are the two rock types most commonly found in this district. They weather down quite differently, both by chemical and physical processes, during exposure to water and extremes of temperature. Quartz grains, in sandstone, are made of silica which does not break down chemically. Sandstones are resistant to

Honeycomb Weathering

chemical weathering when held together with a quartz cement, but wherever the cement is either clay or iron-rich or missing, the sand grains become loose and will be washed out. Variable types of cement result in differential weathering, producing deep, yellow cavities or a honeycomb pattern on some rock faces. This is also apparent where poor quality stone has been used for building, and the rock is exposed to rain and frost. Other minerals such as feldspars and muscovite found in the Millstone Grit will eventually break down to clay particles. Flaggy sandstones with numerous bedding planes will decompose much more readily than a massive quartz sandstone which is resistant enough to produce exposed cliffs and benches.

Shale contains clay particles in finely laminated beds and breaks down easily when exposed. Organic acids produced from plants and rain water react chemically with the shale to speed up the weathering process. Most shale outcrops are hidden by a layer of debris and vegetation.

Freeze-thaw weathering occurs when temperatures fluctuate around 0°C. Water present within pore spaces, along bedding planes and in joints, expands on freezing, causing blocks to fall from cliff faces. Angular blocks form scree slopes which are found below many gritstone edges. Freeze-thaw conditions continue to break down sandstone blocks into quartz grains or fragments. This is why some moorland footpaths appear to be covered with a white sharp sand bleached by acids from the moorland peat.

Sandstone can have a variety of colours. The brown colouration of weathered rock is caused by the oxidation or rusting of iron minerals cementing the particles together. Black surface colouration on the rock results

Scree at Butterley Cutting

Holmbridge Churchyard

from soot being deposited - a legacy of the burning of coal in domestic hearths, mills and factories before the Clean Air Acts of the 1950s. Because the atmosphere now has less soot and dust the buildings are slowly cleaned by acid rain-water, although the rain-wash is more effective on smooth ashlar sandstone than it is on rougher wall stone. Fine ashlar buildings in Huddersfield, such as the Town Hall and the Railway Station, have responded well to being commercially cleaned, with the sharpness of carving and the pale colour of Crosland Moor sandstone (Rough Rock), well displayed enhancing the townscape.

Graveyards are fascinating places for geologists to study. Many headstones are made of the best local sandstones. These are easily worked, with inscriptions often legible after 150 years of weathering. During the 19th century the use of limestone or marble headstones was unfortunate because acid rainwater reacted unfavourably with calcite, etching the polished surface of the stone. The use of lead letters inset into marble headstones is an improvement but as the stone weathers, the letters are loosened and may fall out. There is a long history of the use of exotic stones from other parts of Britain and overseas. Most of these are igneous rocks, such as granites and gabbros, which take a high polish. They are hard and therefore more difficult to letter, and are less prone to most forms of weathering as their crystalline texture has few weaknesses. Their highly polished surfaces do not allow the accumulation of soot or lichens as readily as other rock types. Nowadays many churches place restrictions on the use of these highly polished headstones, preferring local materials.

QUARRYING

The quarrying of sandstone has always been of great value to the economy of the Huddersfield district. Coarse sandstone was shaped into millstones for grinding corn, and the lower part of the Upper Carboniferous period has taken its name, 'Millstone Grit', from this industry.

The value of the rock depends upon how it is bedded and jointed. The best stone has massive bedding, with blocks 2 to 3m thick, and is called 'freestone' because stone masons can work it in any direction with hand tools. Sandstones in beds 30 to 50cms thick can also be used as building stone. Well-jointed beds can be split into bedding closer than 5cms are ideal for flags. Many quarries have a variety of bedding types and therefore produce stone of various qualities.

The earliest quarries produced stone for local use only, due to the high cost of transport. The enclosure of fields in the late 18th century created the demand for stone walls. Much of this stone would have come from clearing the fields, but small quarries would also have provided stone for local buildings, and flagstones for tracks and paths. The 1854 Ordnance Survey maps show hundreds of sandstone and flag quarries, called delve-holes (or delph-holes) throughout this district.

Alison Quarry, Digley

manageable blocks. The Elland Flags, Greenmoor, Grenoside and Rough Rock sandstones are the best local freestones. Irregularly bedded rocks are used as wall stone and rocks with

Some quarries, called 'town's quarries', were opened to exploit stone for building roads in the 19th century and are sometimes recorded in parish deeds.

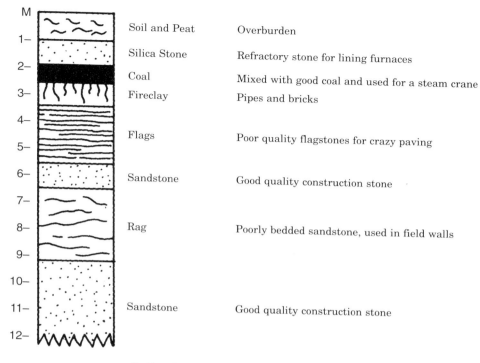

M			
1–		Soil and Peat	Overburden
		Silica Stone	Refractory stone for lining furnaces
2–			
		Coal	Mixed with good coal and used for a steam crane
3–		Fireclay	Pipes and bricks
4–			
		Flags	Poor quality flagstones for crazy paving
5–			
6–		Sandstone	Good quality construction stone
7–			
8–		Rag	Poorly bedded sandstone, used in field walls
9–			
10–			
11–		Sandstone	Good quality construction stone
12–			

Section through Low Edge Quarry, Magnum

Longwood Edge probably had 2 or 3 separate companies working from the 1880s until the 1920s. Crosland Hill quarries became increasingly important in the early part of the 20th century and in 1937 Johnson Wellfield advertised itself as having 11 different quarries covering a large area, producing stone for a variety of purposes. Bingley Quarry, at Holmbridge, was worked by F. Marsden and Sons for at least 20 years from 1881, and the neighbouring Alison Quarry was opened to produce stone to build walls and banks for nearby Digley dam. The Elland Flags were of such excellent quality that they were quarried and mined in the 19th century at Fartown and Fixby, as well as further north, towards Halifax. An example of the varied use of quarried stone obtained from the Rough Rock sequence is Low Edge Quarry, near the old hamlet of Magnum, Hade Edge. This quarry, like many others in the Huddersfield district, would have employed a large number of quarrymen with specific tasks. Delvers, who started the process, were skilled in removing stone from the various beds. Under their direction labourers used picks, wedges and crowbars in the quarry. Large blocks were split using 'plug and feathers'. A straight line (or race) of 60cm deep holes was drilled into the rock. Feathers are metal flanges which fit into the hole, and then a metal wedge (or plug) was gradually knocked into each hole so that the pairs of feathers were widened by a series of mallet blows. The rock then split along the line of tension. This process is still in use today.

Plug and Feathers, Crosland Hill

Splitting Rough Rock at Johnson Wellfield, Crosland Hill

Steam cranes, often fired by local coal from thin coal seams nearby, were used to lift large blocks of stone. Simple devices have been used, since the Roman era, to hold and lift stone blocks. A lewis has a pair of half-round legs, which grip the sides of a drilled hole. When the lifting ring is raised, an angled pull on each leg creates a secure hold. Iron lifting tongs, like over-size scissors, and chain dogs, which are J-shaped hooks joined by a length of chain, grip a stone block using dog holes roughly chiselled into two opposite faces. In Huddersfield town centre, between The George Hotel and the railway over-bridge, the retaining wall is pockmarked with them. These lifting devices enabled the masons to place any stone block directly into its mortar bed, with the underside clear of ropes and slings. Masons working today on York Minster still use the lewis, tongs or chain dogs to handle masonry blocks.

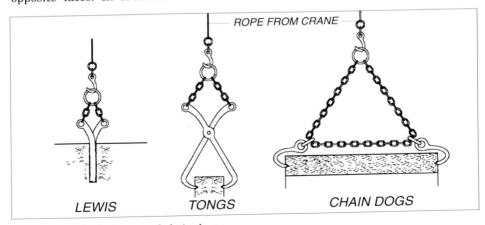

Drawings of Lewis, tongs and chain dogs

Banker (or bench) masons worked at the quarries and shaped the stone as required. Most building stone was pitched with pitching chisels and a hammer which left a squared off block with a rough surface. Better quality stone was dressed and finished (with a fine chisel and a mallet) like ashlar, with tooling marks (on average 8 per 25mm) leaving fine lines on the stone. Dressers, who were skilled stone-masons, shaped and dressed stone to produce sills, headers and lintels. The finest sandstone was cut by sawyers operating sawing frames. Next planers finished the stone to produce ashlar blocks. Gate posts, wall-stone, lintels and mullions often have a variety of tooled surfaces, devised by the masons for decoration.

Quarrymen sometimes came across 'marestones' which are large balls of soft sand and clay, usually coloured dark red, brown or dark yellow (ochre), contained in some beds. Sandstone containing marestone was worthless, but the marestone itself could be manufactured into donkeystone blocks which were used to colour the edges of doorsteps. Marestone from Cook's Study quarry above Holmfirth was cut and used locally or sent to Lancashire to be mixed with cement to make donkeystone blocks. With increasing use of artificial building materials demand for stone decreased, resulting in smaller quarries closing in the 1930s and 1940s. However quarries are still working on Cartworth Moor, Crosland Hill, and in the Shepley area, providing employment for a number of local people.

Ganister, a pure quartz-rich sandstone, has also been important in this district. It was used to make refractory bricks for lining steel furnaces, and was widely quarried. The Chain Quarries between Marsden and Meltham, and the large Royd Edge Quarry, above Meltham, produced ganister for the Meltham Fire-Clay Company. The ganister was ground down for fire-bricks at the company's works near the old Meltham railway station. It employed 300 people, but closed in the 1970s, when the easily-worked ganister in the quarries became exhausted.

Gatepost in Hinchliffe Mill

Brick manufacturers and many collieries exploited the Coal Measure shales associated with coal seams to make bricks for their own use and local sale. The 1884 Directory for Huddersfield lists brick-makers at Lower Cumberworth, Fieldhouse (Fartown), Thurstonland, Kilner Bank (Dalton) and Hazlehead (Crow Edge). By 1909 the most important brick manufacturer was the Huddersfield Brick and Tile Co., at Birchencliffe and Hillhouse Lane, Fartown (where they used glacial clays).

Today shales are extracted at Crow Edge and Shepley for pipe manufacture by Hepworth plc, and Elliotts Bricks, of Kirkheaton, use the shales below the Grenoside sandstones, which they mix with other shales from various quarries to produce high quality domestic bricks in a variety of colours and finishes.

Old Bricks

MINING

IRONSTONE

Mining for iron ore became important in this district in the 12th century, when monks came from Fountains, Byland and Rievaulx Abbeys. The Tankersley Ironstone Bed lies within the Coal Measure shales and is 35cms thick. The monks worked this iron ore along its outcrop towards the north and east, from Bentley Grange, near Emley, which was the main centre of the iron ore industry. Old pit mounds show evidence of iron mining at Bentley Springs.

In the early years of mining the monks used to dig either long trenches or 'bell pits' depending on the depth of the ore. A series of holes or shafts was dug to the depth of the mineral layer, and

Bell-pits at Bentley Springs

then the ore was extracted in all directions forming a bell shape beneath the surface. When the likelihood of roof collapse was imminent the pit would be abandoned. The excavation of a new shaft would then begin a short distance away. Bell pit mining was the only method then available to reach minerals covered by layers of other rock. After the ore had been extracted it was taken to primitive furnaces, called 'bloomeries', situated near to the bell pit workings and made into wrought iron. Nearer to Huddersfield, at Bradley Wood, the Black Bed ironstone yielded ore of great economic value with a 30% iron content. Iron mining was important for about 200 years, but no ironstone has been worked since the 17th century.

COAL

Coal was the other main mineral to be exploited. Mining was started by the monks of Byland Abbey, in the Flockton area, possibly before the 14th century.

As well as the bell pit method miners also dug what were called 'day holes' or 'day eyes'. These were worked by tunnelling a near horizontal adit into the shales from the side of the hill to obtain coal. Often miners who worked bell pits also had their own 'day hole' for domestic use.

Later, the introduction of mechanisation and deeper shafts increased the coal mining industry's extraction of the mineral as it gave access to deeper seams. The coal seams at Huddersfield dip towards the east, concealed by younger rocks. One of the larger coal mines in the district was the Denby Grange pit, north of Flockton, where several shafts were sunk. The pit was worked for 150 years in thin seams less than a metre thick from which a large tonnage of coal was extracted. In 1778 a new lease from the Denby Grange estate enabled more shafts to be sunk nearby which included Caphouse Colliery, now the National Mining Museum for England.

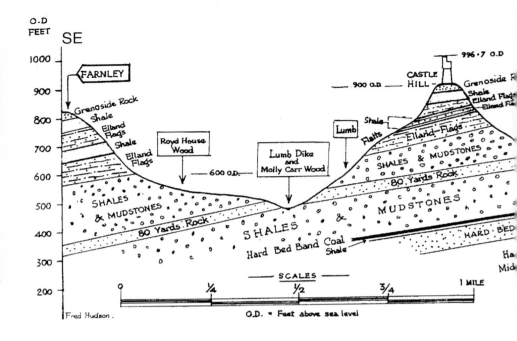

The diagram above shows that there are four main coal seams and a minor seam in the Huddersfield area, between Lockwood and Castle Hill. The coals vary in thickness, hardness and sulphur content. These seams of coal were important in the past as they were mined by local people for domestic fuel. Industry also used local coal in the mills and factories for steam power during the industrial revolution. There were many pits in the Huddersfield area in 1861 and as the coal was mined out new pits opened. Many pits were individually owned, with few families or companies owning more than one pit at a time.

An interesting account of local mining is given in the 'History of Kirkburton' written by Eli Exley (1912). He suggests that mining began "many generations ago" and describes the extent of the industry between 1850 -

1910. In Kirkheaton, there were over thirty collieries of various sizes, employing at least 300 local men, so mining was clearly a major industry. The coal seams are not far beneath the surface, so many of the mines were day-holes, rather than shafts. However some collieries had shafts, the deepest of which was St. Helen's colliery, Moor Lane, with a depth of 50 metres. Coal mining became less important in the Huddersfield area during the first few decades of the century, probably because the seams are generally thin, and so deeper and more efficient mines opened further east towards Wakefield. A few small pits were worked in the Second World War, but only for local domestic consumption.

Coal seams rest on seat-earth which is either a fireclay (mudstone) or a ganister (sandstone). Both may be used for firebricks. They contain numerous

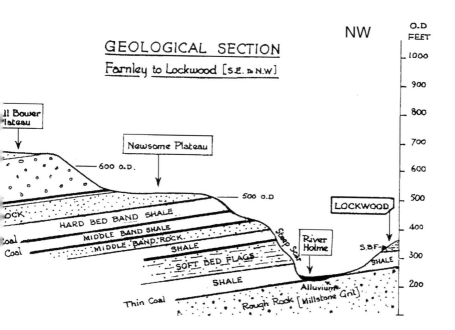

GEOLOGICAL SECTION
Farnley to Lockwood [S.E. to N.W.]

NW

O.D
FEET

1000
900
800
700
600
500
400
300
200

ll Bower Plateau

Newsome Plateau

600 O.D.

500 O.D

LOCKWOOD

OCK
HARD BED BAND SHALE
MIDDLE BAND SHALE
MIDDLE BAND ROCK
SHALE
SOFT BED FLAGS
SHALE
Coal
Thin Coal
River Holme
S.B.F.
SHALE
Alluvium
Rough Rock [Millstone Grit]

fossil roots, being fossil soils (palaeosols) without bedding or lamination. The coal seam itself is made up of layers of differing qualities. The bottom layer is usually softer than the rest, as it is mixed with some of the seat-earth. The 'middle coal' (or 'brights' from its appearance) has less ash, and burns well. The next layer, the 'upper coal', 'hards' (or 'dull coal'), was valued as a good steam coal.

Resting on the upper coal is a layer of shale of varying thickness called 'bind'. This forms the roof of the coal seam and is usually softer than the shale higher up. If the roof shale changes to sandstone it is usually an indication of the seam thinning. The roof shales generally contain many fossils, which help to reconstruct the environment of Coal Measures times.

CLAY

Clay was exploited in this district for pottery manufacture, mostly from seat-earths in the Lower Coal Measures. Suitable clay was found at Lockwood Scar, Lindley Moor and Salendine Nook. In the 13th and 14th century fireclay was worked at Upper Heaton, known at the time as Poter Heton. After the clay had been dug out, local river sand was incorporated to prepare it for pottery manufacture. The potters produced cooking pots, puncheons and jugs which were then traded at local markets. Kilns were built on nearby hills, taking advantage of the prevailing wind, which increased the flue draught and so raised the firing temperature. The Morton family ran the Salendine Nook pottery for 300 years closing only in the 1940's.

WATER

Water, though not regarded generally as of geological concern, has had a profound effect upon this district. From the acid peat uplands flow the headwaters of many rivers and streams. This high ground has an average rainfall of one metre (938mm to 1313mm) per annum whereas Huddersfield town centre had a mean annual rainfall of 814.1mm, in the seven years to 1996 (University data). The soft, pure water flowing from the peat uplands is used in huge volumes by the local textile industry for treating, washing and dyeing wool.

summit level of the canal was vital, as this section always lost water when barges passed through its locks.

The underlying geology is important in the locations chosen for siting reservoirs. The strata must be stable and impervious, and suitable rock and clay needs to be available locally for dam construction.

Natural springs and wells provided water for early settlements but were insufficient to supply drinking water to a growing population. To cater for this need the Victorians built reservoirs which are still in use today and can be seen in many valleys on the eastern

Digley Reservoir looking towards Black Hill

Dams were originally built by mill-owners across the steep-sided valleys to ensure a constant supply of water. As the industrial revolution progressed the demand for water power grew even after the steam engine replaced the water wheel as a power source. Many of the Colne valley reservoirs were built for the Huddersfield Narrow Canal. Maintaining a water supply to the

slopes of the Pennines. Millstone Grit and Lower Coal Measures sandstones are sources of water supply for local mills, factories and breweries, pumping from private springs or boreholes.

GLOSSARY

Anticline A rock fold in the form of an arch.

Ashlar Carefully dressed and squared stonework, with a smooth finish and narrow mortar gaps.

Attrition The rounding of grains of sediment during transport in rivers, because of frequent collisions with other particles.

Bullions Nodules or concretions, roughly spherical or elliptical in shape, produced as a result of early local cementation within a sediment. They often contain fossils which act as a nucleus.

Calcite Common mineral made of calcium carbonate. Chief constituent of limestone and marble. Found as white or colourless crystals and many other forms.

Carboniferous A period of geological time, lasting about 63 million years, from 353my to 290my ago.

Coal Measures A series of sandstones, shales and coal seams laid down in the Westphalian epoch of the late Carboniferous period between 313-302my ago.

Cross-bedding A series of minor bedding planes inclined to the major bedding plane, in a sandstone, showing the direction of current flow.

Dip The angle of inclination of the rock beds measured from the horizontal.

Erosion The process of wearing away a rock or landscape by an agent e.g. a river or an ice sheet.

Feldspar Major rock-forming group of minerals with a high silica content. Usually pink, white or orange. Essential constituent of most igneous rocks. Eroded fragments are often found in Carboniferous grits and sandstones.

Gabbro Dark igneous rock with large crystals composed of feldspars and iron-rich minerals.

Gneiss Banded rocks formed during metamorphism, by heat and pressure.

Granite Coarse-grained igneous rock consisting essentially of quartz, feldspar and mica.

Horizon A particular level in the sequence of rock-strata.

Igneous A group of rocks which form when molten magma cools within the Earth's crust, or as lava at the surface.

Laminated Fine layering in beds of shale, less than 2 millimetres in thickness.

Lithification The process of changing unconsolidated sediment into rock.

Marine band A layer of sediment, noted for its marine fossils such as goniatites and bivalves, and useful for correlating rocks from different areas.

Marine transgression A rise in sea-level or a fall in land-level, so that the land surface is flooded by the sea.

Metamorphic rocks Rocks changed from their original state by a change of conditions, such as a increase of pressure or temperature in the earth's curst.

Millstone Grit series Sandstone and shale series deposited in the Namurian epoch between 323-313 million years ago.

Muscovite A mica mineral occurring primarily in acid igneous rocks, but often deposited in Carboniferous sandstones and grits after erosion.

Namurian An epoch in the Carboniferous period lasting about 10 my, about 323 my ago.

Pyrite Mineral (iron sulphide) often found in shales and coal seams.

Quartz Crystalline silica mineral, widely-distributed rock-forming mineral, very hard and resistant to weathering.

Sandstone Sedimentary rock formed of lithified sand grains with a mineral cement.

Seat-earth Horizon of pale clay (fire-clay) or white sand (ganister) below a coal-seam, which represents the sediment or soil in which the swamp vegetation grew.

Sedimentary rocks Rocks formed of sand and mud, derived by weathering of pre-existing rocks. Deposited by rivers, winds or the sea, then lithified to form solid rock.

Shale Fine-grained, laminated sedimentary rock, composed of clay particles.

Silica The mineral material SiO_2 from which quartz is made.

Weathering The breakdown of rocks in situ, by physical, biological or chemical processes.

Westphalian The epoch in the Carboniferous period, following the Namurian, which lasted about 11my, from 313-302 million years ago.

BIBLIOGRAPHY

Ordnance Survey Map Sheffield & Huddersfield. **Sheet 110** 1:50,000

Geological maps Glossop. **Sheet 86** 1:50,000 *British Geological Survey.* Huddersfield. **Sheet 77** 1:50,000 *British Geological Survey.* Remapping sheet 77 1997-1998.

Further reading

The Pennines and Adjacent Areas - *British Regional Geology* - 1954 HMSO.

Guide to the Building Stones of Huddersfield. - 1994 *Huddersfield Geology Group.*

Yorkshire Rock. Richard Bell - 1996 *British Geological Survey.*

Technical references

BISAT, W.S. 1924 The Carboniferous goniatites of the north of England, and their zones. *Proceedings of the Yorkshire Geological Society* Vol 20 p.40-124.

BROMEHEAD, C.E.N., EDWARDS, W.N., WRAY, D.A., & STEPHENS, J.V. 1933 Geology of the Country around Holmfirth and Glossop. *British Geological Survey* Memoir Sheet 86.

GILLIGAN, A. 1920 The petrography of the Millstone Grit of Yorkshire. *Quarterly Journal of the Geological Society* Vol. 75 p.251-294.

GOODCHILD, J. 1983 Caphouse Colliery and the Denby Grange Collieries. *Wakefield Historical Publications.*

HOLMES, D.H. 1967 The Mining and Quarrying Industries in the Huddersfield District. *Tolson Museum , Huddersfield.*

WIGNALL, P.B. and MAYNARD, J.R. 1996 High-resolution sequence stratigraphy in the early Marsdenian (Namurian, Carboniferous) of the central Pennines and adjacent areas. *Proceedings of the Yorkshire Geological Society.* Vol.51 Part 2, p.127-140.

WOODWARD, A.S. 1916 On a New Species of *Edestus* from the Upper Carboniferous of Yorkshire. *Quarterly Journal of the Geological Society* Vol 72 p.1-6.

WRAY, D.A. 1929 The Mining Industry in the Huddersfield District. *Tolson Museum Handbook* No6, p1-24, *Huddersfield.*

WRAY, D.A., STEPHENS, J.V., EDWARDS, W.N., and BROMEHEAD, C.E.N. 1931 Geology of the Country around Huddersfield and Halifax. *British Geological Survey* Memoir. Sheet 77.